THIS IGLOO BOOK BELONGS TO:

igloobooks

Published in 2019
by Igloo Books Ltd
Cottage Farm
Sywell
NN6 0BJ
www.igloobooks.com

GOL002 1218
2 4 6 8 10 9 7 5 3 1
ISBN 978-1-78905-654-9

Written by Stephanie Moss
Illustrated by Louise Forshaw

Designed by Lee Italiano
Edited by Nicholas Oliver

Printed and manufactured in China

MONKEY MISCHIEF

igloobooks

Marvin Monkey was so sure he was the best trickster around.
OO-OO! he always sang, as he swung above the ground.

"There's no one in the jungle
that can play tricks quite like me."

"I can trick anyone I want," he called,
"but just who will it be?"

He **BANGED**
a coconut together

and woke the parrots
from their nap.

... and landed in
a rhino's lap.

He tickled Leopard with a feather and made him sneeze.

The flamingos **SQUAWKED**

when he stuck them in the lagoon with superglue.

One day, as Marvin Monkey sang his usual song,
a cheeky monkey called Maddie came swinging along.

"There's no one in the jungle," he sang,
"that can play tricks like me!"

OO-OO!
"That's what you think," said Maddie.
"Just you wait and see!"

Marvin couldn't believe it. He set to work straight away.
He had a trick for Crocodile that he'd saved for such a day.

"I've got some bubblegum," said Marvin.
"If you want some, you're in **luck**!"

POP! BURST! SMACK!

went Crocodile, until his jaws were completely **stuck**.

Maddie crept near the **SNORING** zebras,
when they were having a snooze.

This was one trickster contest that she wasn't going to lose.

She painted them all white, so they weren't stripy any more.

Tiger GROWLED
when Marvin teased him
with a tasty pretend treat.
Lion ROARED
when Maddie decorated the
sharp claws on his feet.

He blew bubbles at the hippos.

he Scared Elephant by Shouting,

"BOO!"

But it was Gorilla that said,

"I'VE HAD ENOUGH OF THOSE TWO!"

"Here, here!"
CHEERED all the animals.
"But we can't sit here and moan."
"If we want to stop them both,
we need a great trick of our own."

So Snake **HISSED** at them next morning,
"Come to our carnival tonight!"

The monkeys couldn't wait.
They'd trick every animal in sight!

Marvin and Maddie's heads were spinning with all the tricks that they could try.
There was dancing and laughter as the carnival got in full swing...

They **HOWLED**, **SCREECHED** and **GIGGLED** as the animals passed by.

... when, **suddenly**, the lights went out and the monkeys couldn't see a thing.

There was SCUFFLING behind them. Marvin cried,
"Put the lights on, please!"
"GOTCHA!" cried the animals.
"Who knew that pranks were such a breeze?"

"Oh, no, we're trapped!" cried Maddie.
"Our tails are tied together!"
"Yes!" the animals laughed. "Do you
promise to stop playing tricks forever?"

"Yes, we're sorry," said the monkeys. "Our trickster days are done."
"Though playing tricks on each other could be even more fun!"

So Marvin and Maddie's pranks on the animals all came to an end.

They each agreed it would be much better tricking a cheeky best friend!